Mein erster Grieg
My First Grieg

Die leichtesten Klavierstücke von
Edvard Grieg

Easiest Piano Pieces by
Edvard Grieg

Herausgegeben von / Edited by
Wilhelm Ohmen

Coverillustration: Silke Bachmann

ED 23397
ISMN 979-0-001-21221-2

www.schott-music.com

Mainz · London · Madrid · Paris · New York · Tokyo · Beijing
© 2021 Schott Music GmbH & Co. KG, Mainz · Printed in Germany

Edvard Grieg
Steckbrief

1843	geboren am 15. Juni in Bergen
	Den ersten Klavierunterricht erhält er als Sechsjähriger von seiner Mutter, die Pianistin war. Bei Hauskonzerten lernt er die Musik von Schumann, Mendelssohn und Chopin kennen.
1858	Studium am Leipziger Konservatorium u.a. bei Ignaz Moscheles (Klavier) und Carl Reinecke (Komposition)
1863	Übersiedlung nach Kopenhagen. Hier lernt er den Komponisten Richard Nordraak kennen, der ihm die norwegische Volksmusik nahebringt. Sie wird seine Kompositionen entscheidend beeinflussen.
ab 1866	In Kristiana, dem heutigen Oslo, wirkt er als Pianist und leitet die Philharmonische Gesellschaft.
1867	Heirat mit der Sängerin Nina Hagerup
1869	Ein Reisestipendium, angeregt durch Franz Liszt, ermöglicht ihm eine Kunstreise durch Deutschland und nach Rom. Hier trifft er Liszt, der seine Werke sehr schätzte.
1874	Vom norwegischen Staat erhält er einen Ehrensold, der es ihm erlaubt, als freischaffender Komponist zu wirken. Bis zum Ende seines Lebens unternimmt er zahlreiche Konzertreisen innerhalb Norwegens und in die europäischen Musikmetropolen.
1880–1882	Dirigent der Musikgesellschaft in Bergen
1885–1907	Grieg lebt in Bergen. Die Sommermonate verbringt er in seiner Villa *Troldhaugen* südlich von Bergen, dem heutigen Grieg-Museum.
1907	Er stirbt am 4. September an einer Lungenkrankheit.

Vorwort

Edvard Grieg wird als der wichtigste norwegische Komponist angesehen. Mit seiner Musik bildet er bewusst einen Gegenpol zur deutschen Romantik. Für die norwegische Volksmusik ließ er sich begeistern, was seiner künstlerischen Entwicklung und seinem musikalischen Schaffen eine entscheidende Wendung gab. Dieser volkstümlich gefärbte Stil in seinen Kompositionen hat ihm in der Musikwelt bis heute große Popularität verschafft. Zudem förderte er maßgeblich die nationale norwegische Musiktradition. Seine Konzertreisen durch Europa waren sehr erfolgreich. Hier knüpfte er Freundschaften u.a. mit Johannes Brahms und Peter Tschaikowsky.

Grieg komponierte u.a. zahlreiche Werke für Klavier, davon allein 66 *Lyrische Stücke*, Kammermusiken und Vokalwerke. Zu Henrik Ibsens Theaterstück *Peer Gynt* schrieb er die Bühnenmusik. Bekannt und beliebt sind die beiden Orchestersuiten daraus, ebenso die Suite *Aus Holbergs Zeit* für Streichorchester und sein viel gespieltes berühmtes *Klavierkonzert in a-Moll*.

Der vorliegende Band enthält 17 der insgesamt 66 *Lyrischen Stücke*. Sie sind von leicht bis mittelschwer einzustufen. Aus der ersten *Peer Gynt Suite* wählte ich die beliebte *Morgenstimmung* (in einer vierhändigen Fassung) und *Åses Tod* aus. *Solvejgs Lied* aus der zweiten Suite beschließt den Band.

Die Metronom-Angaben sind Vorschläge des Herausgebers, die individuell den Fähigkeiten des Spielers und dem Charakter der Musik angepasst werden können.

Wilhelm Ohmen

Edvard Grieg
Biography

1843	born in Bergen on 15 June
	His mother was a pianist and gave him his first piano lessons when he was six years old. At private performances the young Edvard heard music by Schumann, Mendelssohn and Chopin.
1858	began studies at the Leipzig Conservatoire with teachers including Ignaz Moscheles (piano) and Carl Reinecke (composition)
1863	moved to Copenhagen.
	There he met composer Richard Nordraak, who introduced him to Norwegian folk music: this was an important influence on Grieg's compositions.
from 1866	In Christiana, now Oslo, he worked as a pianist and conducted the philharmonic orchestra.
1867	marriage to the singer Nina Hagerup
1869	A travel scholarship made possible by Franz Liszt enabled Grieg to tour Germany and travel to Rome. There he met Liszt, who admired his music.
1874	An honorary bursary from the Norwegian state enabled him to work as a freelance composer. Until the end of his life he made numerous concert tours in Norway and to the musical capitals of Europe
1880-1882	conductor for the Music Society in Bergen
1885-1907	Grieg lived in Bergen. He spent the summer months in his villa *Troldhaugen* south of Bergen, which is now the Grieg Museum.
1907	Grieg died of lung disease on 4 September.

Preface

Edvard Grieg ranks as the most important of all Norwegian composers; his music represents a deliberate contrast to German Romanticism. He was an enthusiastic proponent of Norwegian folk music, which had a decisive influence on his artistic development and creative output. The flavour of folk music made his compositions popular in the musical world to this day – and made a significant contribution to promoting the Norwegian national musical tradition. In the course of very successful concert tours across Europe he formed friendships with other musicians including Johannes Brahms and Peter Tchaikovsky.

Grieg's compositions included numerous works for the piano, among them 66 *Lyric Pieces*, as well as chamber music and vocal works. He wrote the incidental music to Henrik Ibsen's play *Peer Gynt*: the two orchestral suites taken from that work have remained popular. Equally well-loved is the Suite *From Holberg's Time*, which Grieg wrote and then arranged for string orchestra, and his famous and much-played Piano Concerto in A minor.

This book includes seventeen of the 66 Lyric Pieces, at an easy to intermediate level. From the first Peer Gynt Suite I have chosen the popular *Morning Mood* (in an arrangement for four hands) and *The Death of Åse*. *Solveig's Song* from the second suite appears at the end.

Metronome markings are suggestions by the editor and may be adapted to suit the abilities of each player as well as their interpretation of the music.

Wilhelm Ohmen
Translation Julia Rushworth

Inhalt / Contents

Arietta
op. 12/1

Edvard Grieg
1843–1907

Poco andante e sostenuto (♩ = 88)

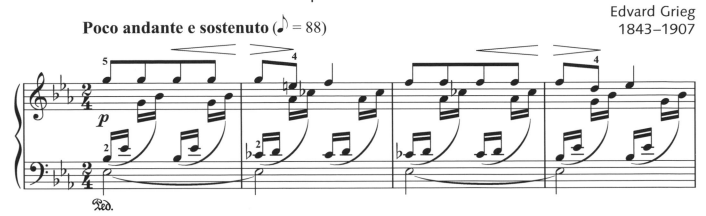

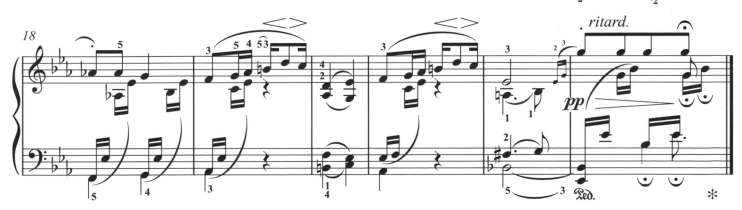

Walzer / Waltz

op. 12/2

Edvard Grieg

Allegro moderato (♩ = 150)

Coda

Wächterlied / Watchman's Song

op. 12/3

Edvard Grieg

Molto andante e semplice (♩ = 100)

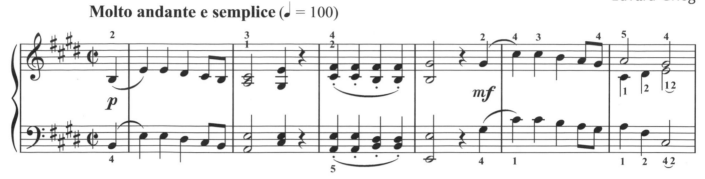

Intermezzo (Geister der Nacht)

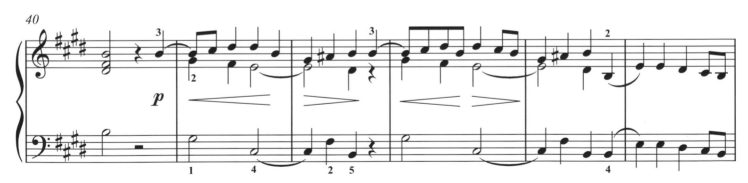

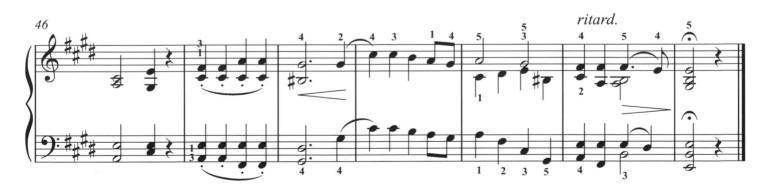

Elfentanz / Fairy Dance
op. 12/4

Molto allegro e sempre staccato (♩. = 54-60)

Edvard Grieg

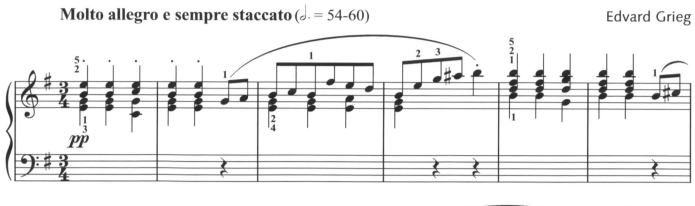

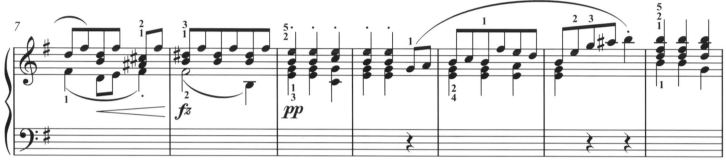

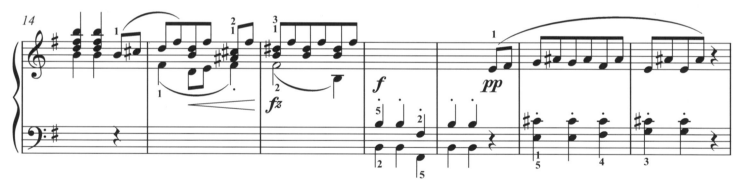

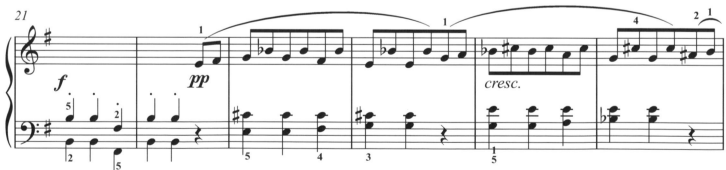

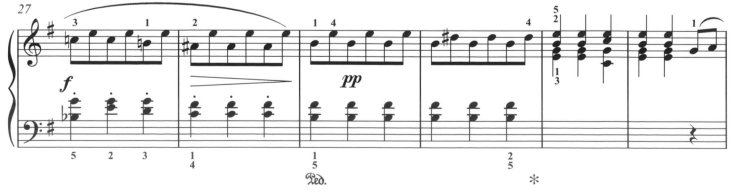

Norwegisch / Norwegian

op. 12/6

Edvard Grieg

Presto marcato (♩ = 132)

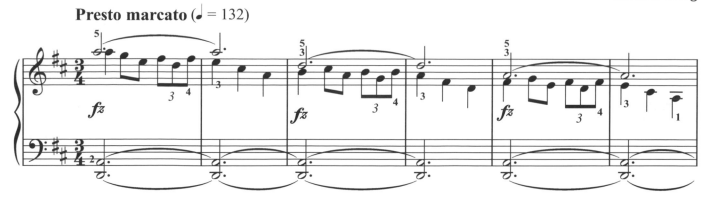

Albumblatt / Album Leaf

op. 12/7

Edvard Grieg

Allegretto e dolce ($\quarternote = 66$)

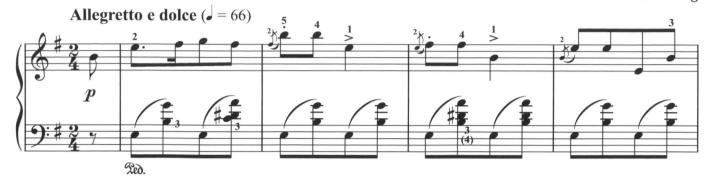

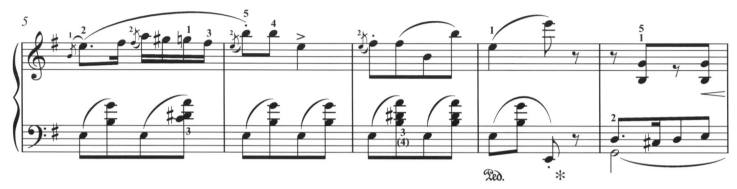

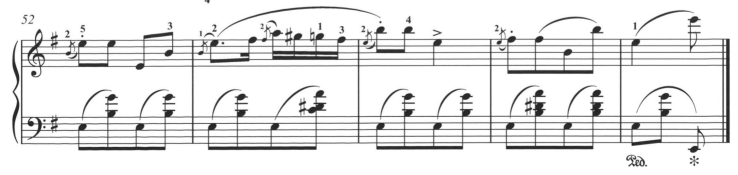

Vaterländisches Lied / National Song

op. 12/8

Edvard Grieg

Maestoso (♩ = 100)

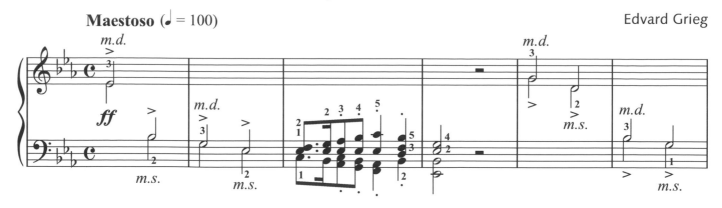

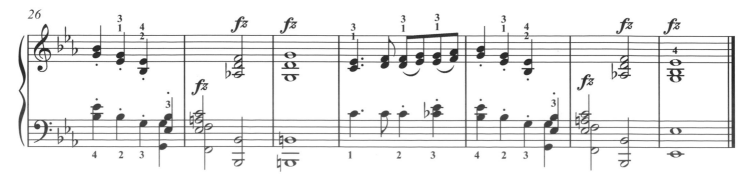

Kobold / Puck

op. 71/3

Edvard Grieg

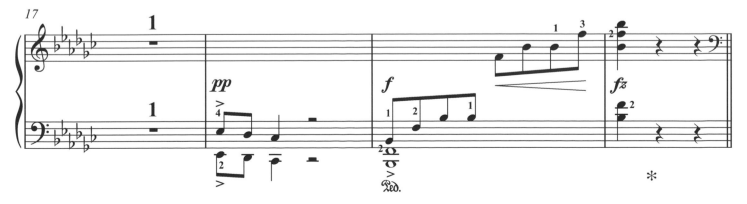

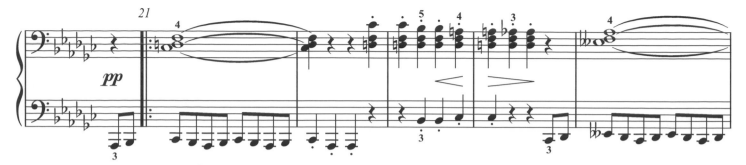

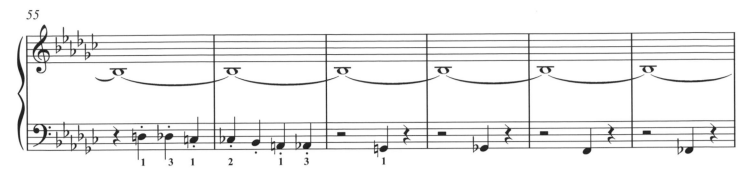

Volksweise / Folksong

op. 38/2

Edvard Grieg

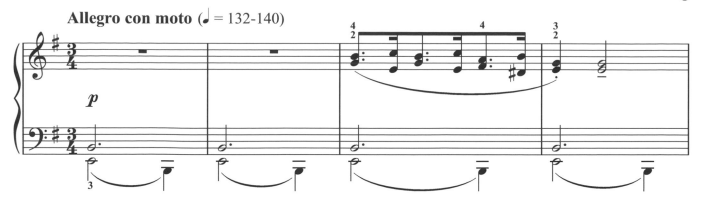

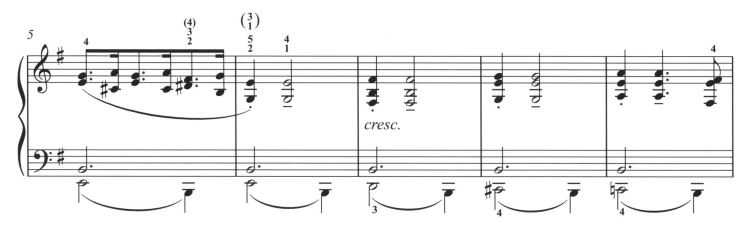

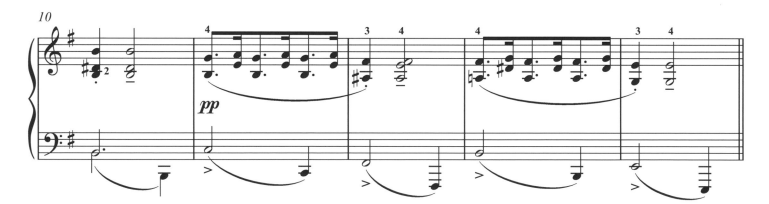

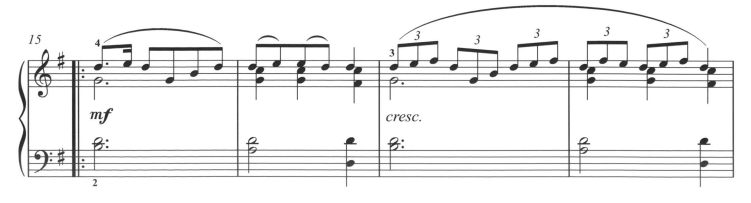

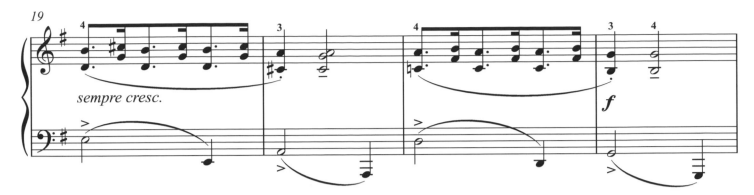

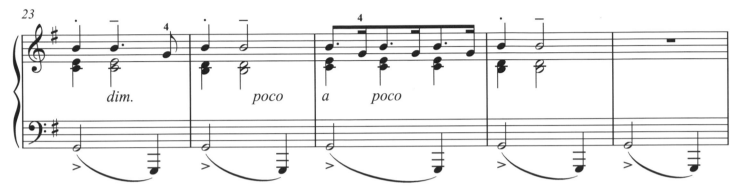

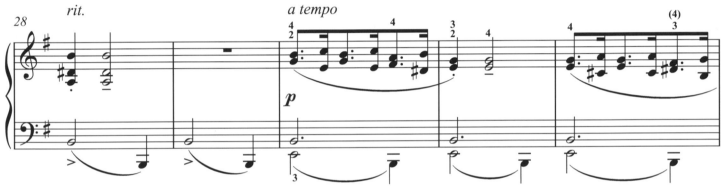

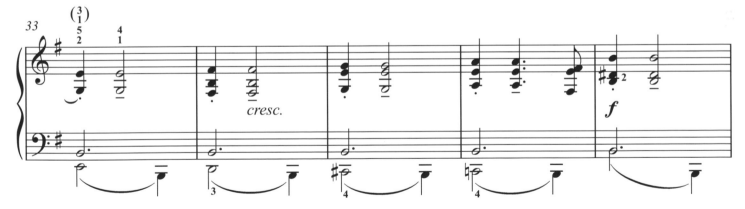

Springtanz / Leaping Dance
op. 38/5

Edvard Grieg

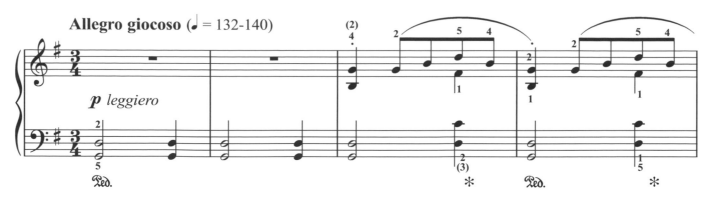

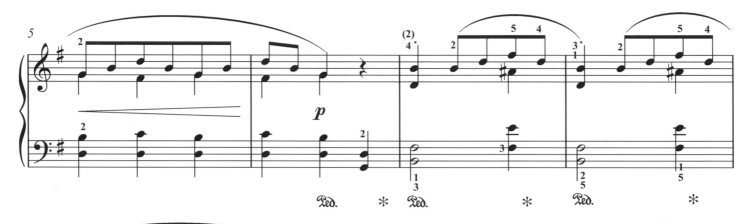

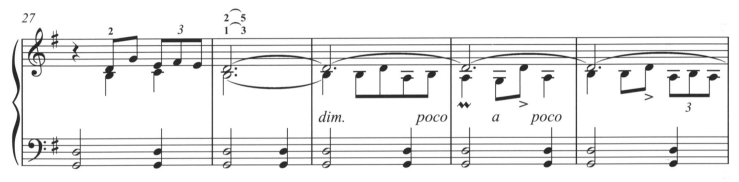

Walzer / Waltz

op. 38/7

Edvard Grieg

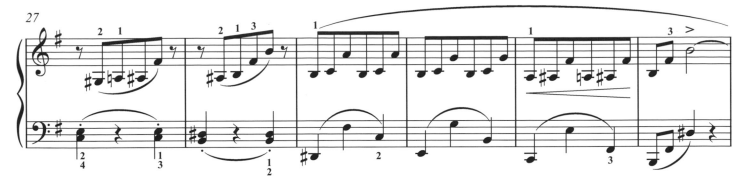

Tempo I   *ritard.*

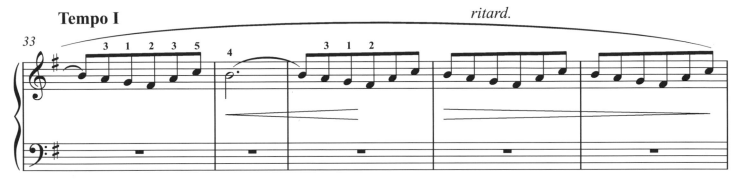

a tempo

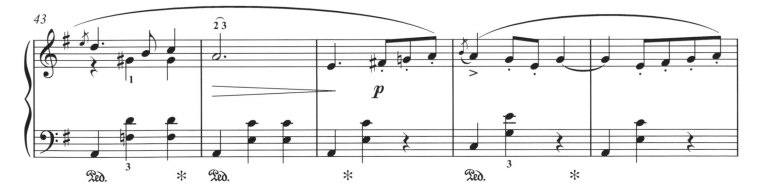

ri - - - tar - - - dan - - - do   **Lento**

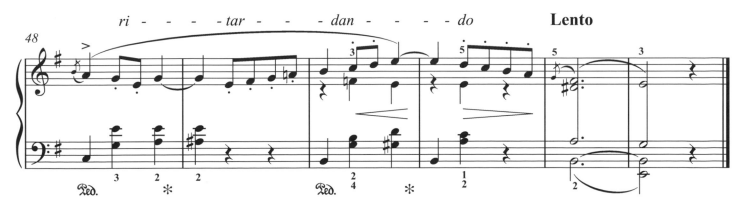

Schmetterling / Butterfly
op. 43/1

Edvard Grieg

Allegro grazioso (♩ = 100)

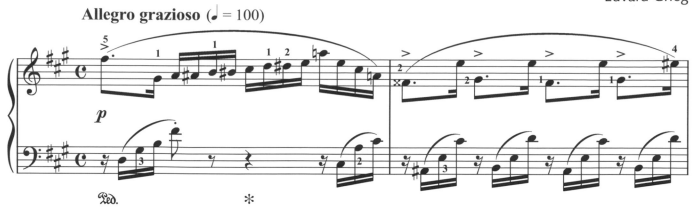

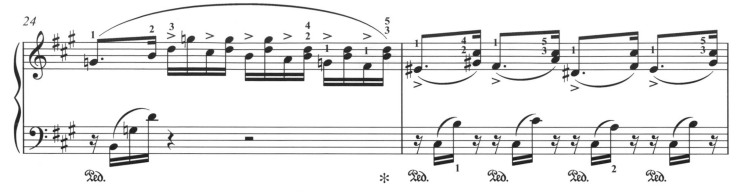

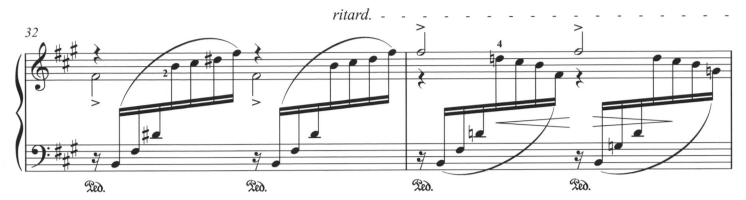

Einsamer Wanderer / Solitary Traveller

op. 43/2

Edvard Grieg

Allegretto semplice (♪ = 126)

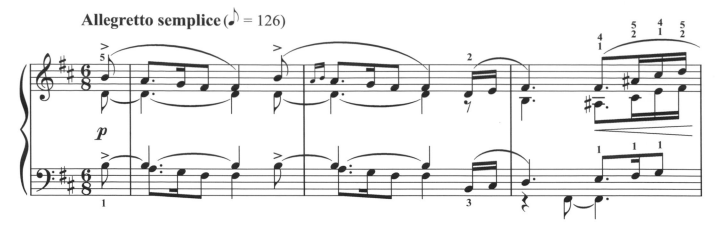

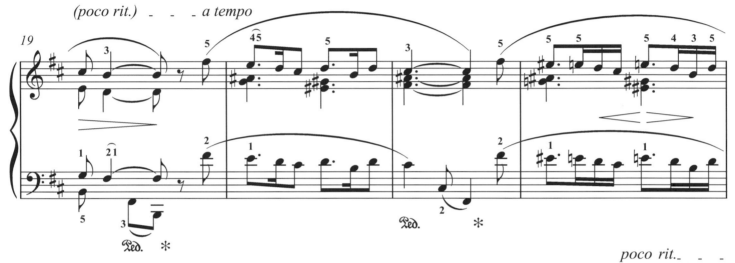

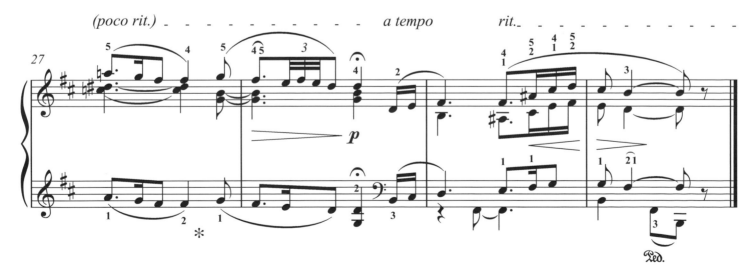

Melodie / Melody

op. 47/3

Edvard Grieg

Allegretto (♩. = 66)

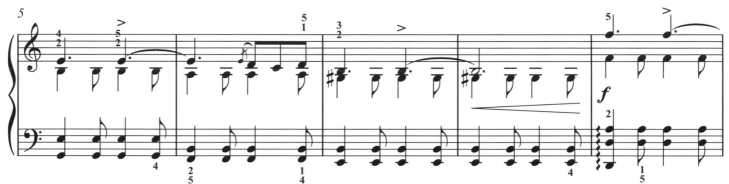

Più mosso

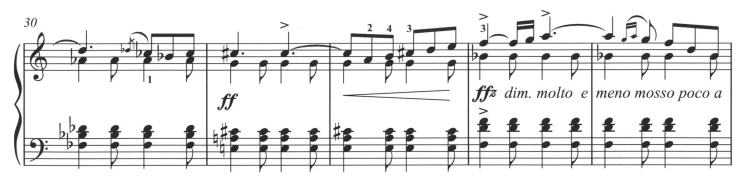

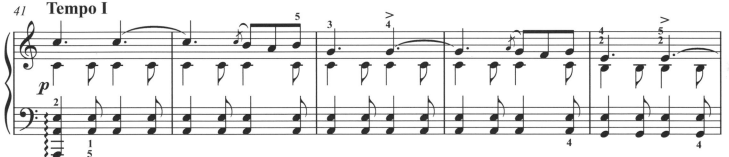

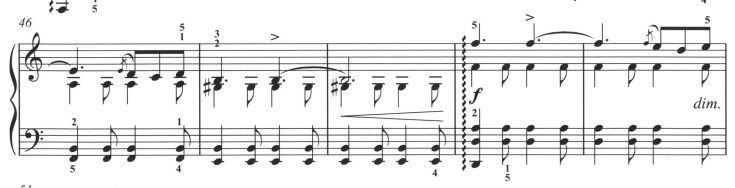

Più mosso

Tempo I

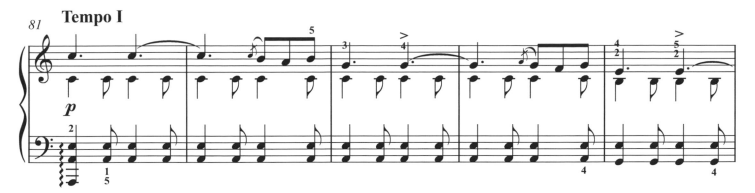

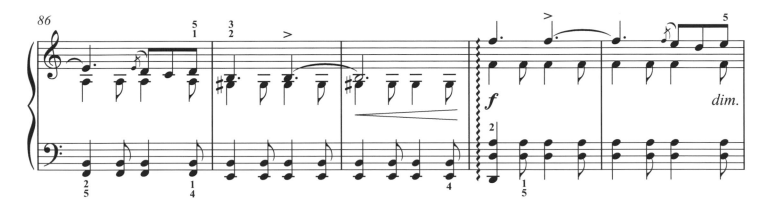

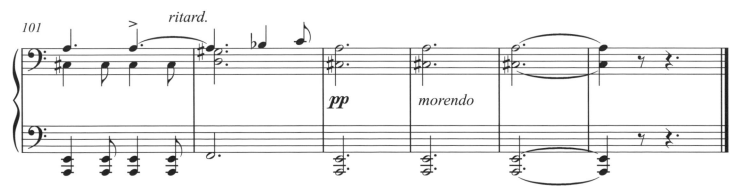

Notturno

op. 54/4

Edvard Grieg

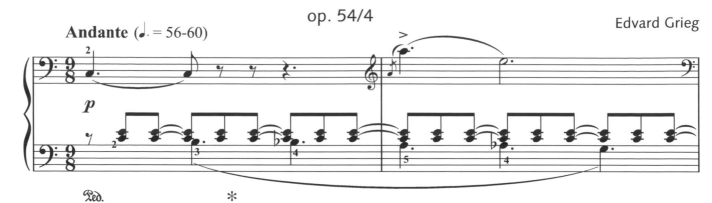

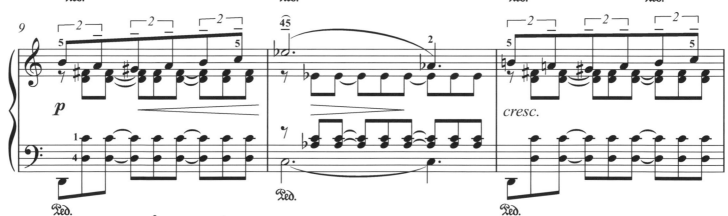

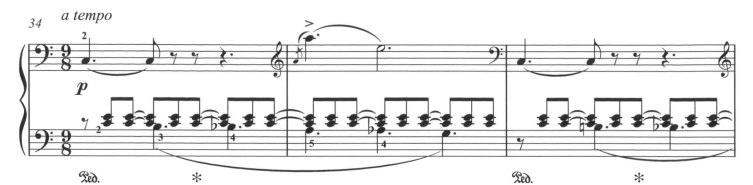

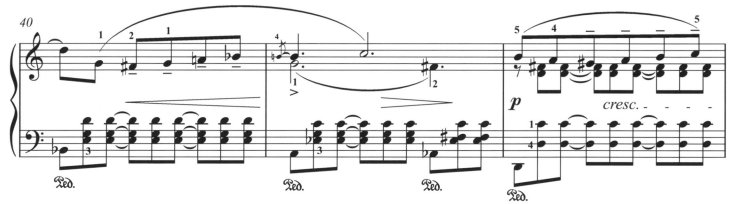

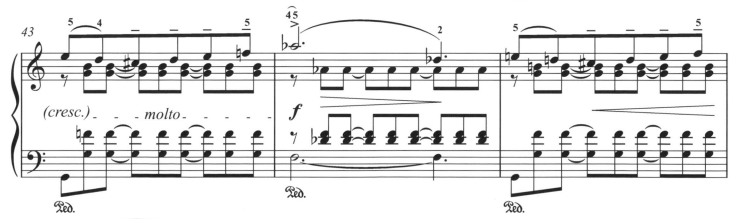

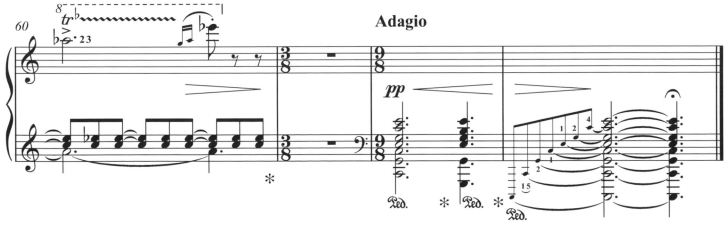

Matrosenlied / Sailors' Song

op. 68/1

Edvard Grieg

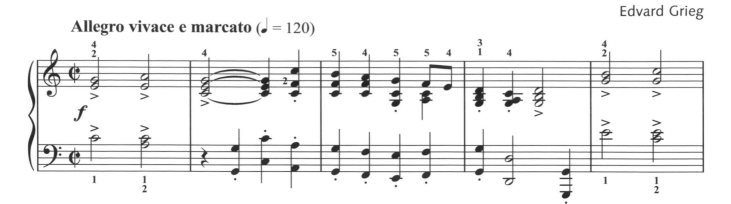

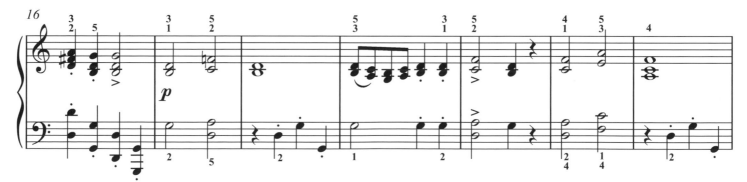

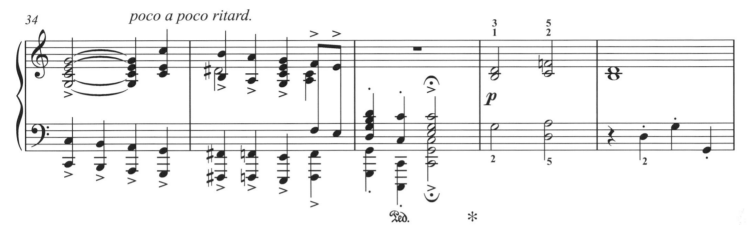

Nachklänge / Remembrances

op. 71/7

Edvard Grieg

Tempo di Valse (♩. = 54)

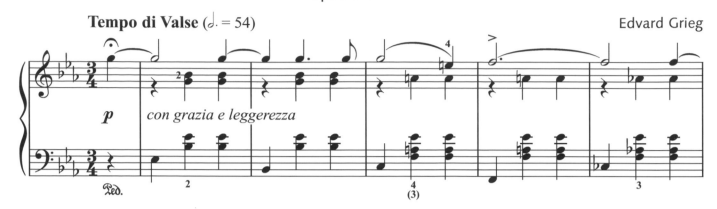

p — *con grazia e leggerezza*

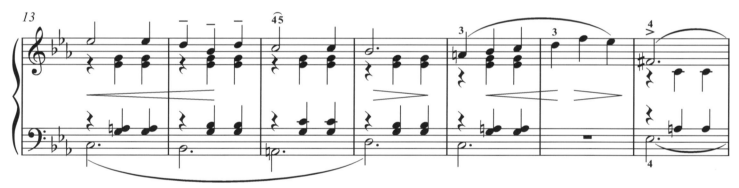

poco rit. — *a tempo*

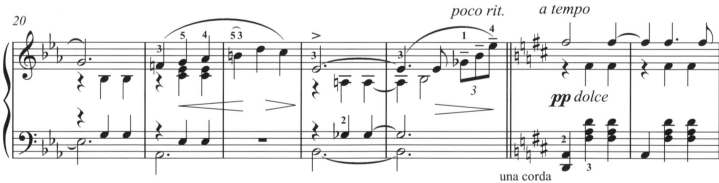

pp dolce

una corda

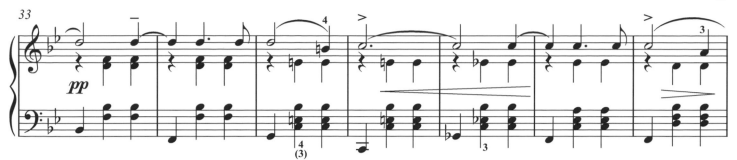

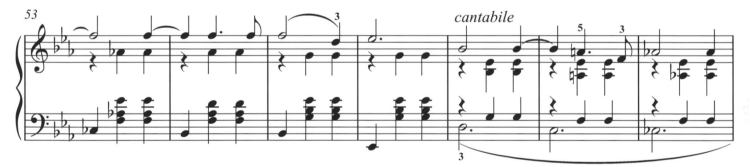

Secondo
Morgenstimmung / Morning Mood
op. 46/1

(vierhändig / four hands)

Edvard Grieg
Arr.: Edvard Grieg

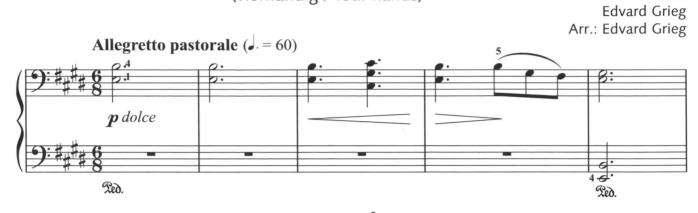

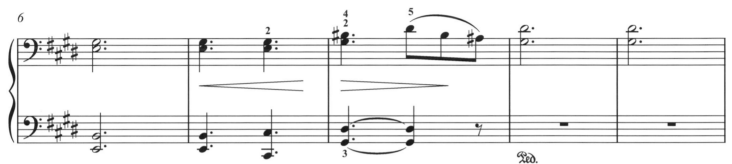

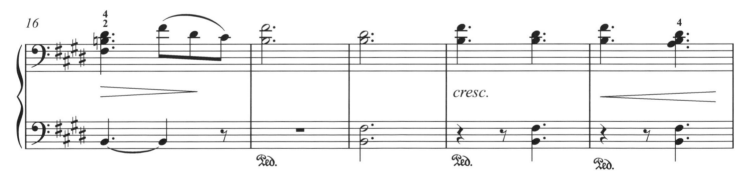

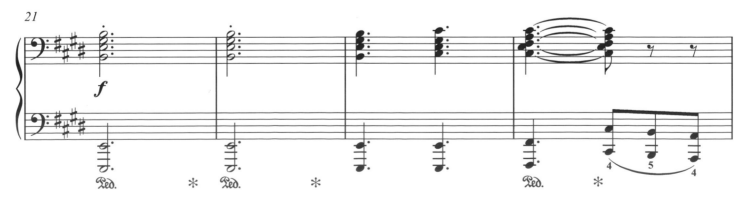

Morgenstimmung / Morning Mood

op. 46/1

(vierhändig / four hands)

Edvard Grieg
Arr.: Edvard Grieg

Allegretto pastorale ($\,\!.$ = 60)

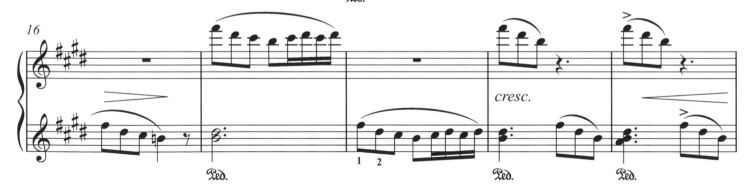

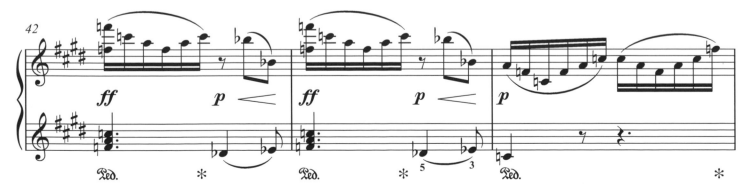

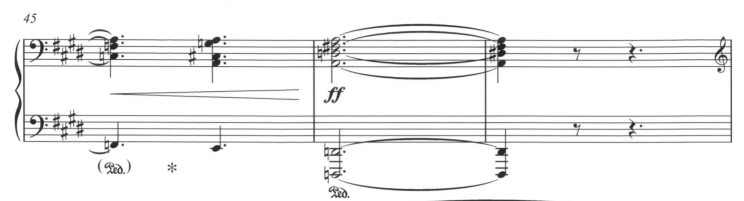

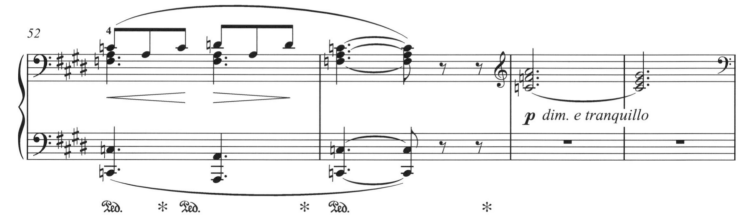

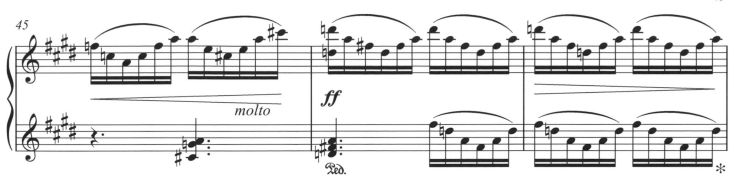

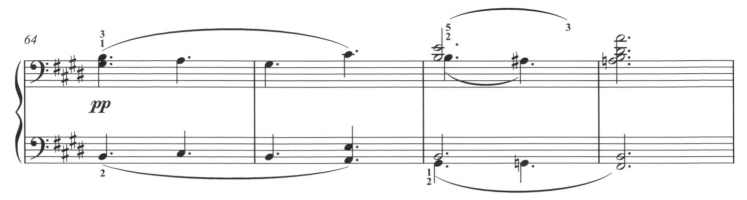

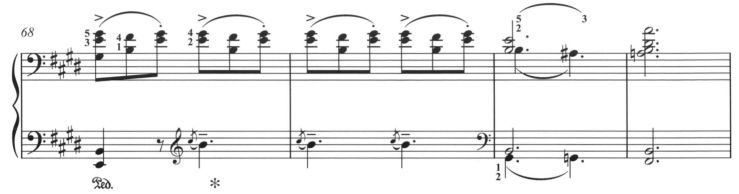

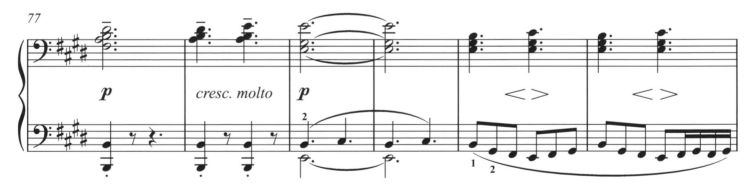

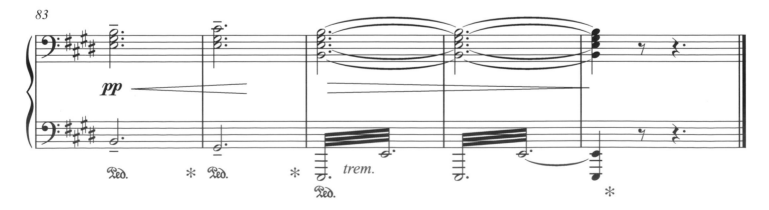

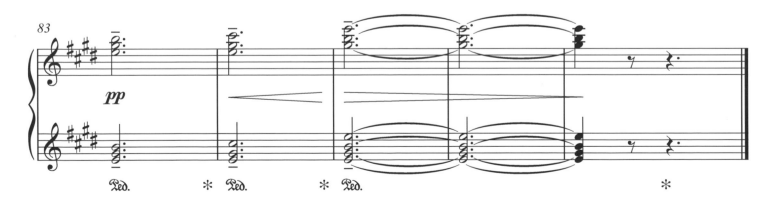

Åses Tod / The Death of Åse

op. 46/2

Edvard Grieg
Arr.: Edvard Grieg

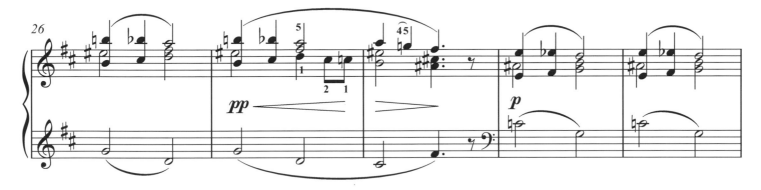

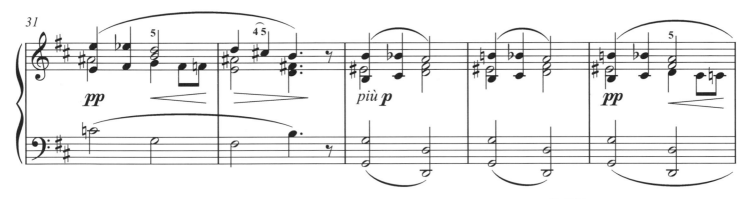

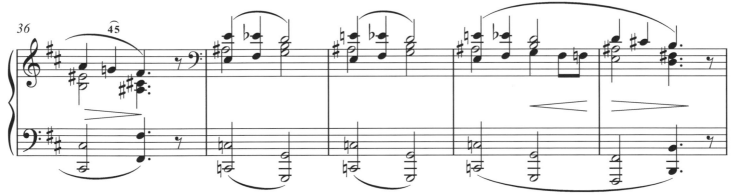

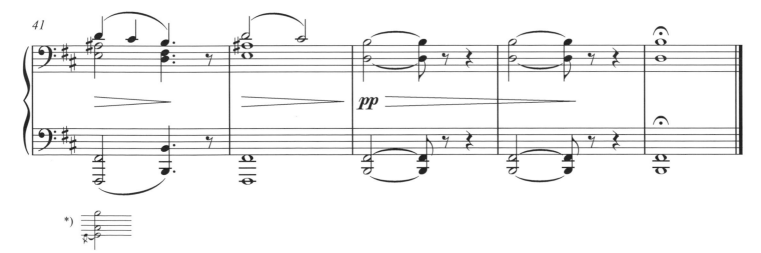

Solveigs Lied / Solveig's Song

op. 55/4

Edvard Grieg
Arr.: Edvard Grieg

Allegretto tranquillamente (♩ = 120)

poco rit.   **Andante (Tempo I)**

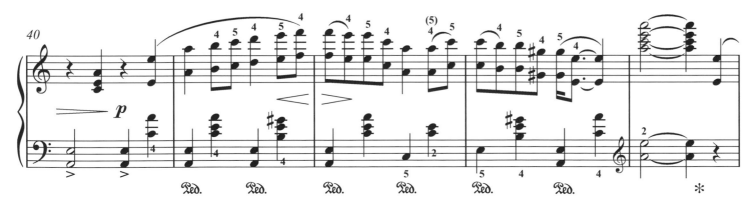

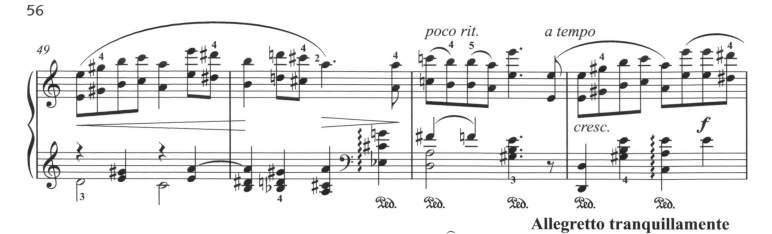

Allegretto tranquillamente

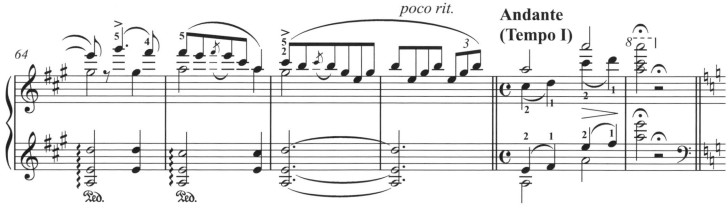

Andante
(Tempo I)

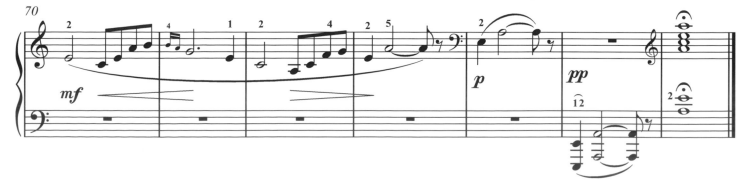